Teddy Ruxpin Lullabies II

More Dreamy Songs for Sleepy Time.

Lyrics by:	Ken Forsse
Music Composed by:	George Wilkins
Illustrated by:	Russell Hicks
	Theresa Mazurek
	Lisa Souza
	Fay Whitemountain

WORLDS OF WONDER™

Worlds of Wonder, Inc. is the exclusive licensee, manufacturer and distributor of the World of Teddy Ruxpin toys.
"The World of Teddy Ruxpin" and "Teddy Ruxpin" are trademarks of Alchemy II, Inc., Chatsworth, CA.
The symbol W•W and "Worlds of Wonder" are trademarks of Worlds of Wonder, Inc., Fremont, California.

Grubby® Newton Gimmick™ Princess Aruzia™ Leota™ Wooly What's-It™ Prince Arin™ Fobs®

"A Quieter Place To Be"

There's a quieter place to be,
Where we go when we get sleepy.
There's a quieter place to be,
And it's time for going there.

With a lullaby and a kiss good night,
We'll soon be on our way.
Rest your tiny head. Now say, "good night."
It's been a long, long day.

So sink into the covers
And cuddle up real tight.
It's time to put the day away.
It's time to say, "good night."

"And I Love You"

You're warm and you're friendly
And I love you.
And you are very good to me.

You're happy skipping stones
Or watching rain fall.
And you are very good to me.

There's something very special
When your smile gets very wide.
There's something very special
When we're by each other's side.

You're warm and you're friendly
And I love you.
You are very good to me.

You're warm and you're friendly
And I love you.
And you are very good to me.

You say you like to do
The things that I do.
And you are very good to me.

There's something very special
In the way you hold me tight.
There's something very special
In the way you say, "good night."

You're warm and you're friendly
And I love you.
You are very good to me.

It only takes a minute,
Every now and then,
To let me know how much
You care for me.

And when you show me every day
In, oh, so many ways,
It makes it clear that you and I
Should be together.

You're warm and you're friendly
And I love you.
And you are very good to me.

You're happy taking walks
And chasing rainbows.
And you are very good to me.

The beauty and the laughter
Just sparkle from your eyes.
And when you start to go to sleep
It makes me realize:

You're warm and you're friendly
And I love you.
You are very good to me.

"Sheep Of Different Colors"

When it is time for me to go to sleep,
It helps a lot to count a flock of sheep.

But when I close my eyes,
When daytime turns to night,
Those sheep that jump across the bed
Don't have to be just white.

Chorus

There are sheep of different colors
That jump across my bed:
Some green, some blue and yellow,
Some orange, some red.

For each and every color
I imagine in my head,
Can be the colors of the sheep
That jump across my bed.

There goes an orange sheep,
And there goes one that's blue.
The yellow one is pretty,
The red one's pretty, too.

A pink one with a purple nose,
A grey one's tail is green,
More color combinations
Than I have ever seen.

Repeat Chorus

There's a chartreuse sheep with silver hooves,
One's iridescent blue,
An aqua and a turquoise one,
A two-toned brown one, too.

A red one with pink polka-dots,
A lavender one, too,
A tan one with vermilion stripes,
A ewe of every hue.

And as I watch those jumping sheep,
I start to realize,
Those colors blend together
If I tightly close my eyes.

And then the green and orange,
And yellow, blue and red
Become a lovely rainbow
Right here above my bed.

Chorus

There are sheep of different colors
That jump across my bed:
Some green, some blue and yellow,
Some orange, some red.

For each and every color
I imagine in my head,
Can be the colors of the sheep
That jump across my bed.

"Tiny Friend Of Mine"

Just close your eyes,
Tiny friend of mine.
It's time now for you to be sleeping.

Just close your eyes,
Tiny friend of mine.
Today is a memory we'll be keeping.

The lavender shadows that cover the nighttime
Are moving across the sky.
It's cozy and comfortable under the covers.
It's time now to close your eyes.

Just close your eyes,
Tiny friend of mine.
The sunshine has turned to starshine.

Just close your eyes,
Tiny friend of mine.
The day's given way to the coming of nighttime.

The wind that is blowing the leaves of the meadow
Is helping the night birds fly.
Get cozy and comfortable under the covers,
It's time now to close your eyes.

Spring turns to summer, then into autumn
And winter is close behind,
Just as the daytime is followed by nighttime
When we close our eyes,
Tiny friend of mine.

Just close your eyes,
Tiny friend of mine.
It's time now for you to be sleeping.

Just close your eyes,
Tiny friend of mine.
Today is a memory we'll be keeping.

The blue crystal moonlight that paints all the nighttime
Shines down from a lovely sky,
While each star is seeing how bright it can sparkle,
It's time now to close your eyes.

Just close your eyes,
Tiny friend of mine,
And dream all the dreams you've been keeping.

Just close your eyes,
Tiny friend of mine.
Tomorrow's just waiting when you've finished sleeping.

The beauty and laughter that shines from inside you
Helps me realize
All the ways that I love you, my sweet tiny friend.
It's time now to close your eyes.

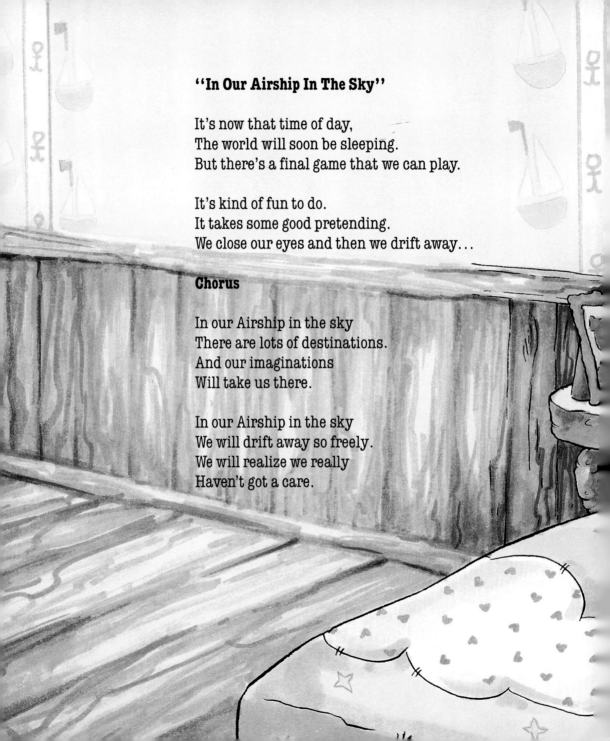

"In Our Airship In The Sky"

It's now that time of day,
The world will soon be sleeping.
But there's a final game that we can play.

It's kind of fun to do.
It takes some good pretending.
We close our eyes and then we drift away...

Chorus

In our Airship in the sky
There are lots of destinations.
And our imaginations
Will take us there.

In our Airship in the sky
We will drift away so freely.
We will realize we really
Haven't got a care.

The patchwork bag that pulls
Our Airship high into the sky
Looks like the quilt
That covers up your bed.

It's round and kind of puffy
And very, very soft,
Just like the pillow
Where you lay your head.

We'll guide the ship so carefully
Between the cotton clouds,
And drift on every breeze
That comes your way.

We'll watch the nighttime shadows
Move across the land below,
And hear the echoes
Of the passing day.

Chorus

In our Airship in the sky
Let's dream a place to visit.
We will see there really isn't
Any place too far.

We can sail around the world.
We can find the land of daydreams.
We can stop and play with moonbeams.
We can sail up to a star.

We'll guide the ship so carefully
Between the cotton clouds,
And drift on every breeze
That comes your way.

We'll watch the nighttime shadows
Move across the land below,
And hear the echoes
Of the passing day.

Chorus

In our Airship in the sky
Come with me and we will travel,
And we'll carefully unravel
All the wonders on the way.

In our Airship in the sky,
There will be no place for sorrow
And we'll be back by tomorrow,
Just to start a brand new day.